THE CITY & GUILD

FOOD SAFETY TRAINING MANUAL

Level 2 Award in Food Safety in Catering

PETER J. JARRETT

City&
Guilds

About City & Guilds

City & Guilds is the UK's leading provider of vocational qualifications, offering over 500 awards across a wide range of industries, and progressing from entry level to the highest levels of professional achievement. With over 8500 centres in 100 countries, City & Guilds is recognised by employers worldwide for providing qualifications that offer proof of the skills they need to get the job done.

Equal opportunities

City & Guilds fully supports the principle of equal opportunities and we are committed to satisfying this principle in all our activities and published material. A copy of our equal opportunities policy statement is available on the City & Guilds website.

First edition 2013
Reprinted 2014, 2015

ISBN 978 0 85193 237 8

Publisher Louise Le Bas
Cover design by Select Typesetters Ltd
Typeset by Integra Software Services Pvt. Ltd
Printed in the UK by Cambrian Printers Ltd

British Library Cataloguing in Publication Data

A catalogue record for this book is available from the British Library' on the page before contents, under Copyright.

Publications

For information about or to order City & Guilds support materials, contact 0844 534 0000 or centresupport@cityandguilds.com. You can find more information about the materials we have available at www.cityandguilds.com/publications.

Every effort has been made to ensure that the information contained in this publication is true and correct at the time of going to press. However, City & Guilds' products and services are subject to continuous development and improvement and the right is reserved to change products and services from time to time. City & Guilds cannot accept liability for loss or damage arising from the use of information in this publication.

City & Guilds
1 Giltspur Street
London EC1A 9DD

T 0844 543 0033
www.cityandguilds.com
publishingfeedback@cityandguilds.com

CONTENTS

ACKNOWLEDGEMENTS

Picture credits
Every effort has been made to acknowledge all copyright holders as below and publishers will, if notified, correct any errors in future editions.

123RF Stock Photo: © robbiverte p29; **Andrew Buckle/City & Guilds:** p16; **Ascobloc:** p38; **Corbis:** © Don Paulson p13, © Lester V. Bergman p8, © Jeffrey Green Photography p31, © Ocean pp18, 31, © Renee Comet Photography p41; **Electrolux:** pp6-8, 21-22, 37-38; **Exclusive Ranges Ltd:** p18; **Fermod:** p34; **Integra:** pp9, 12, 19, 37-38, 40; **iStockphoto:** © Angelika Schwarz p6, © Catherine Yeulet p31, © Hongqi Zhang p42, © Oleksandr Pekur p28, © Steve Cady p28; **Lincat:** pp8, 19, 40; **Monika:** pp7, 27; **Nigel Snell:** pp9, 10, 25, 28, 34, 40; **Nisbetts Plc:** pp10, 13, 19, 21-23, 35; **Peter J. Jarrett:** pp10, 17, 23, 30, 32, 39; **Science Photo Library:** © Cordelia Molloy p28, © SCIEPRO p9, © Gilbert S. Grant p15; **Shutterstock:** © Aletia p6, © Christian Jung p32, © kzww p16, © Mau Horng p15, © Mirumur pp9-10, 30, © OLHA TOLSTA p6, © Pakhnyushcha p16, © Prapann p28, © Winai Tepsuttinun p15; **Standex Food Service Equipment:** p24; **StockFood:** © Paul Williams p31; **TM Electronics:** p41; **Value Marketing:** p20; **Williams Refrigeration:** pp36, 40.

PREFACE

This book is intended for anyone who handles or prepares food, especially students and people working in the catering and hospitality industries. *The City & Guilds Food Safety Training Manual* is written to be an integral learning companion for those studying food preparation, as the steps in the HACCP section can easily be brought into practical recipe development.

It will prepare all students for the Level 2 Award in Food Safety in Catering, plus with the knowledge of HACCP ensure that all food preparation units operate in accordance with European legislation and the Food Standards Agency, and it provides an essential foundation for the Level 3 Award in Supervising Food Safety in Catering.

Further, this book is recommended reading for all persons with responsibilities for managing food preparation operations, to give them an understanding of the resources necessary to maintain food safety.

This book has been written in an easy to understand style, so that any person whose work involves contact with food preparation departments can be aware of everyday hazards and know how to keep food safe for consumption.

INTRODUCTION

Food safety is important. Food poisoning is not just a short temporary illness. It can kill or leave people with permanent disabilities. You may have heard of the E. coli (*Escherichia coli*) 0157 outbreaks; this bacterium produces a very dangerous toxin, a poison that causes severe damage to the kidneys and ulceration of the large intestine.

Elderly people, young children, those in hospital and pregnant women are all more susceptible to food poisoning, because their immune systems (their defence mechanism against bacteria) are not working very well.

The first thing to understand is that food poisoning bacteria are invisible; you cannot detect them by sight or smell. The bacteria that you may detect because food is smelly and slimy are *food spoilage bacteria*, which are in the process of breaking down and spoiling the food. Dangerous bacteria, called *pathogens* because they cause illness, are undetectable and in many cases only a very few bacteria (less than 10) are required to cause an infection and make people seriously ill.

Bacteria do not remain the same; they evolve to become better at surviving, so we are constantly discovering new types, some of which are resistant to antibiotics and medical treatment.

Bacteria can appear anywhere, and for many reasons. We think of foods such as melons as being safe, yet in the USA growing cantaloupe melons were fertilised with raw sewage that contained an antibiotic-resistant salmonella bacterium. The result: four people died. Bacteria are a *hazard*, which is why special attention must always be paid to ready-to-eat foods, such as melons, which can be eaten without going through a safety process such as cooking (which can kill bacteria). We are required to only serve food that is safe. People expect and deserve safe food, not illness.

A food item cannot tell you what has happened to it, how it has been cleaned, cooked or stored. Also, as you now know, you cannot tell, just by looking at the food, whether it has been contaminated. It is therefore easy to see how important it is to keep records about the age of food, how it has been stored and at what temperature, and so on, for yourself and others.

Keeping records is part of a food safety system called the *hazard analysis critical control point* (HACCP), which sounds much more complicated that it actually is in practice. As in all work it is important to do things properly and nothing is more vital in the food industry than ensuring people are not made ill by the food they eat. HACCP is a system we work to, in order to be as certain as possible that bacteria stand no chance of reaching our customers or *ourselves*.

Those involved in food preparation can become ill as well: a clean kitchen does not necessarily mean a safe kitchen. Poor working practices such as not washing hands can result in dangerous bacteria contaminating food and causing illness. Therefore it is important that we work to a system that avoids contamination and allows us to be confident that we have handled food correctly, and that system is HACCP.

The laws controlling the preparation of food (see page 24) inflict severe penalties on those who are proved to have served unsafe food, and the food safety and hygiene regulations require that you record your working procedures so that you can show you have handled and prepared food correctly and safely. Record-keeping shows *due diligence* (it shows that you have worked correctly) to others and is an important part of the HACCP system.

FOOD POISONING

Most cases of food poisoning are the result of people not working properly in the kitchen, 'taking chances' and not paying proper attention to the delivery and storage of food. This is why training is important, so that you know what you are doing and are following a safe system when handling and preparing food *at all times*. That system is HACCP.

There are many causes of food poisoning, all of which are avoidable. Let's look at the most common causes:

1   Contamination of food by bacteria and viruses, due to not washing hands frequently, especially after sneezing or visiting the toilet, and in between handling raw meats and ready-to-eat food such as salads.

2   Not heating food sufficiently to kill bacteria.

3   Holding food: keeping it not hot enough (above 63°C) for too long a period, which allows bacteria to grow.

4   Not keeping food cold in the refrigerator, allowing bacteria to grow in a warm environment.

5   Contaminating food, which will not be cooked, with bacteria. This is why we keep cooked and raw food separate.

6   People carrying bacteria. This may be in the form of an infected boil or cut. Some people can carry dangerous bacteria without any sign of being ill.

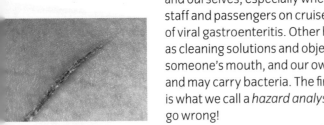

Bacteria are not the only living hazard. *Viruses* are found in shellfish and ourselves, especially when living in close quarters – for example, staff and passengers on cruise ships can suffer from outbreaks of viral gastroenteritis. Other hazards include chemicals such as cleaning solutions and objects such as steel wire that can cut someone's mouth, and our own hair, which can easily fall into food and may carry bacteria. The first step in good practice and HACCP is what we call a *hazard analysis* – or simply, let us see what can go wrong!

BACTERIA: THE NUMBER ONE ENEMY

As always it is important to know your enemy! We control the growth of, and therefore contamination by, bacteria by understanding how they live and die.

Bacteria are single-celled organisms that reproduce (grow) by splitting in half. They have the ability to multiply very quickly at room temperature, given the right environment. They can double as fast as every 10 minutes and so reach more than a million in about three hours, yet even a million bacteria can fit on a pinhead and are invisible.

How do we stop bacteria from growing? By restricting their environment, by removing their food, by making their food unavailable and by using temperature. *Chilling* slows bacteria down, *freezing* causes them to become dormant, *cooking* kills them, and *hot holding* prevents their growth.

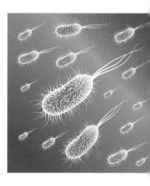

All this can be abbreviated as FATTAM: food, acidity, temperature, time, air and moisture.

Bacteria: FATTAM

Growth limiting factors

F   **Food**

A   **Acidity / pH**

T   **Temperature**

T   **Time**

A   **Air / atmosphere**

M   **Moisture / water**

Bacteria need food
ie your waste

- *Food:* by keeping the kitchen, utensils and work surfaces clean there will be no food available for bacteria. Food debris and grease on the other hand are a breeding ground for bacteria and attract pests.
- *Acidity:* low pH or acid pH liquids such as vinegar and lemon juice are preservatives. Bacteria thrive in a pH of around 5, therefore high pH liquids (above pH 7), such as sanitisers, are used to kill bacteria.

Bacteria enjoy a pH of 5-6+
Eggs, meat and cream

Danger Zone

- *Temperature:* bacteria grow well at room temperature, but can survive throughout the 'dangerous' temperature zone of 5°C to 63°C. This is why we always keep food refrigerated or frozen, heat it to kill bacteria or hold it at a temperature above 63°C to prevent bacteria from growing. All bacteria are destroyed at temperatures above 75°C, which is known as the *critical control point* (ie the safe temperature) for all processed and reheated foods.

Bacteria double
every 20 minutes

- *Time:* bacteria need time to grow, which is why we keep food in the kitchen only for the shortest time possible for preparation, after which we return it to the refrigerator or cook it. Cooking time is also important because the higher the temperature and the longer food is cooked the more bacteria are destroyed.

Bacteria need air

- *Air (atmosphere):* like all living organisms bacteria need air to grow and survive. Unlike us, some bacteria are able to breathe both oxygen and carbon dioxide. We can control bacteria by removing air or packing food with other gases such as nitrogen.

Bacteria need water

- *Moisture:* all living creatures require water, which is why all cleaning surfaces and utensils must be dried. High concentrations of sugar prevent bacteria from accessing any available water; this is why foods such as jam and honey are called *preserves*.

By applying the above safety measures we can keep food safe and fresh, which also has the advantage of avoiding costly wastage.

However, bacteria can survive in very extreme conditions – for example, they do not die when frozen but merely become dormant (ie inactive). Some bacteria, when cooked to a 'killing temperature', first form spores that survive. When the temperature drops to anywhere in the dangerous zone (5°C to 63°C), the spores open and the bacteria begin to grow and multiply. One such example is *Bacillus cereus*, which is a hazard in rice.

Which bacteria cause illness? They are traditionally divided in to two groups: those that live and breed on our food and those that are carried by the food itself. The following table shows the different bacteria relevant to food safety.

Bacteria	Type	Sources	Symptoms and Time
Salmonella	Food poisoning Many types including antibiotic resistance	Raw meat, eggs, poultry, pests, pets and carriers (people carrying the bacteria without showing symptoms of the disease) Raw vegetables, especially those grown with non-pasteurised sewage	Onset: usually 12 to 36 hours Abdominal pain and watery diarrhoea can be deadly, especially antibiotic-resistant varieties
Staphylococcus aureus	Food poisoning that is antibiotic resistant	Carried by people, found in the nose, ears and in boils and cuts (Note: this is why you must always wash your hands after touching your face)	Onset: usually 1 to 7 hours Vomiting and diarrhoea, which can last up to 24 hours
Clostridium perfringens	Food poisoning	Faeces (both human and animal), soil, raw meat and carried by insects	Onset: 8 to 12 hours Abdominal pain and diarrhoea, rarely vomiting
Clostridium botulinum	Food poisoning Produces a deadly toxin	Dirt, soil, fish and improperly prepared foods such as canned fish and pâtés	Onset: 12 to 36 hours, but can be much faster and very serious The toxin can cause paralysis, quickly leading to death
Bacillus cereus	Food poisoning Produces a poisonous toxin	Commonly found in rice and cereals It is a spore forming bacteria, so when rice is not hot-held or reheated properly the spores can be active and so can cause food poisoning	Onset: 12 to 24 hours Abdominal pain with diarrhoea This bacteria can also produce the toxin in the body and so it can take approx. 1 day to start and will last for 2 days
Campylobacter jejuni	Foodborne Most common cause of food poisoning	Found especially on raw poultry, meat, unpasteurised milk Carried by birds and animals, also found in sewage and water Often the result of cross-contamination of poultry coming into contact with ready-to-eat foods such as salads	Onset: 2 to 5 days with abdominal pain, diarrhoea and nausea with fever Most importantly, it is a pre-condition for Guillain-Barré Syndrome, which is a serious neurological disease
E.coli O157:H7	Many varieties exist– the dangerous types are hypermutants Normal wild E. coli is a friendly bacteria that helps the digestion of food	Found in the intestines of cattle that can easily contaminate raw meats, especially hamburgers Animal faeces are used as sewage so it can contaminate ready-to-eat foods including salads, (lettuce and spinach) and is carried by soil on vegetables Can also grow with salad shoots, which have caused major outbreaks	Onset: 3–4 days Bloody diarrhoea starts with abdominal pain Can cause kidney failure, colon ulceration and death due to the dangerous toxin
Listeria	Food poisoning	Found in unpasteurised cheeses and pâté, processed foods and vacuum-packed foods Carried in soil, sewage, water and by animals Can grow at refrigerator temperatures	Vomiting, diarrhoea, fever and potentially death Very dangerous for pregnant women as it can cause stillbirths
Typhoid	Foodbourne, highly contagious	Found in untreated, contaminated water and sewage Can cause serious outbreaks	Onset: 8 to 14 days Fever, serious diarrhoea, headaches and, if untreated, death

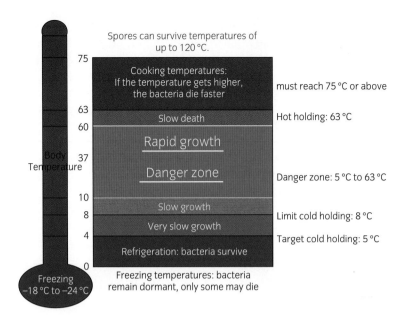

Life cycle thermometer for bacteria

Your best weapon in controlling bacteria is *temperature* (see diagram above).

To recap:

- At *freezing* temperatures bacteria are dormant (–18°C to –24°C).
- At *refrigeration* temperatures bacteria grow very slowly (1°C to 5°C).
- At *room temperature* bacteria grow normally (5°C to 63°C).
- At *cooking temperatures* bacteria are killed. They begin to die off at temperatures above 63°C and all bacteria are killed at 75°C.
- However, spores can form and will still survive temperatures up to 120°C.

SPORES AND TOXINS

Spores are a bacteria's survival package. Some bacteria, when faced with adverse conditions such as rising temperatures, will form a survival spore. This has a protective shell which will withstand higher temperatures than those we reach in cooking. As you know, water boils at 100°C so most of our cooking will only be a little hotter, but spores can survive temperatures of up to 120°C. When the heat returns to room temperature the spore opens and the bacteria start growing to form another colony. This is why *hot holding* at temperatures above 63°C prevents spores becoming active, whereas rapid cooling does not give them a chance to open. Two common spore-forming bacteria are *Clostridium perfringens* and *Bacillus cereus* (see table on page 11). Some foods such as red kidney beans simply need to be cooked to break down the toxins and render them harmless.

Some toxins are produced by careless defrosting (eg scombrotoxin). Toxins are poisons that are produced by bacteria and plants. Toxins can be deadly, such as that produced by *Clostridium botulinum*. The verocytotoxin produced by E. coli 0157 H7 and its relatives causes damage to the kidneys and the intestine, which may result in death, especially in the elderly and the young. Seafood can contain dangerous toxins, one of which causes paralytic shellfish poisoning (PSP), which, as it name implies, causes paralysis. Shellfish such as mussels feed on smaller animals that produce this toxin. In large groups these animals can be seen as a red bloom known as 'red tide'. There are monitoring systems, such as satellite images, that warn where and when shellfish must not be harvested.

Red tide colours the sea, so the toxin can be monitered by satellites

Plants can contain toxins and toxins are produced by moulds. These toxins include aflatoxin, which can seriously harm the liver. Such toxins are found in cereals and dried fruits that have been poorly stored. All these examples demonstrate the importance of always obtaining quality food from reputable suppliers.

The following table shows the hazards that spores, toxins and viruses bring to food preparation.

Spores Toxins Viruses	Type	Sources	Symptoms
Norovirus/ Norwalk virus/ Small round virus	Highly contagious virus passed from person to person	People infected with the virus and items infected people have touched Personal hygiene and frequent hand washing are necessary	Fever, headaches, vomiting and diarrhoea
Spores	Certain bacteria form spores which are a protective survival package when experiencing adverse conditions such as cooking	Clostridium perfringens – spores survive cooking; typically found in sauces and soups that have not been cooled quickly Bacillus cereus – often found in rice that has not been cooled quickly or served immediately	Abdominal pain and diarrhoea
Fish toxins	Paralytic shellfish poisoning (PSP) – found in mussels Scombrotoxin – found in processed fish	PSP – only purchase from reputable suppliers; warnings are issued not to harvest mussels, etc if PSP may be present – usually summer, especially the late summer months Scombrotoxin – care required in defrosting frozen fish, especially smoked mackerel	PSP – tingling sensation leading to paralysis of the limbs and eventually to respiratory failure and death Scombrotoxin – nausea, vomiting diarrhoea, headaches
Bacterial toxins	Once consumed some bacteria produce toxins internally Other types of food poisoning are caused by consuming the toxin directly	E. coli (Escherichia coli) O157:H7 (and other types) produce a verocytotoxin that damages the kidneys, and ulcerates the colon in a condition called HUS. Clostridium botulinum can produce a deadly toxin	E. coli – permanently damaged kidneys need dialysis, removal of the ulcerated colon and death Clostridium botulinum – paralysis and death

PESTS

You may not at first think of mice and cockroaches as dangerous – but they are! For example, a child died after drinking warm milk made from a powder that had been contaminated by mouse faeces. More restaurants are closed because of pest infestation than for any other reason. It is always a sign of a poorly-run kitchen and low, dangerous standards.

Have you ever seen pests or signs of pests in a kitchen or a place where food is stored? Pests will always try to set up home where they can find warmth and food; kitchens are ideal. So, do *not* make pests welcome: always clean as you go, and clean completely at the end of each shift so that all food debris is removed. Food left behind cabinets and in those awkward nooks and crannies can too easily become an invitation for pests to move in.

Pests are dangerous

COCKROACHES

Cockroaches are highly skilled survivors, with 300 million years of experience, so we have to be very careful not to allow them to become residents where food is prepared. A colony is soon started as each egg case carries more than 30 eggs; worse, their legs carry more than 40 different types of bacteria and as many as 12 disease-causing pathogens.

Cockroaches hide behind cabinets, in cracks and pipe ducts, in the walls and under the floors of buildings. These insects enjoy a warm environment (not surprisingly kitchens and boiler rooms are their favourites) and are most active at night. Their presence can be detected by a dry, dusty, mouldy smell, smear marks and pellets of faeces. Any food that is even suspected of being in contact with a cockroach must be discarded.

A colony of cockroaches should be immediately destroyed by a professional exterminator. The names and addresses of reputable exterminators should be easily accessible to senior staff so that an appointment can be made as soon as possible. If you see any signs of cockroaches you must immediately tell your supervisor.

Cockroaches' leg hairs can carry harmful bacteria

RODENTS

Rodents (ie rats and mice) leave tell-tale signs: droppings, gnaw-marks, holes in cereal bags and nesting sites, and of course there is the sighting of dead or living animals themselves. Rodents will be attracted to food stores where they can do considerable damage, and they carry dangerous bacteria which contaminate any food they come into contact with.

If you find such damage, dispose of *all* supplies you think may have been contaminated. Sturdy plastic containers should always be used for cereals such as rice and flour to prevent any pest chewing through the original paper containers.

You must report any rodent signs or sightings immediately to your supervisor who will engage a professional exterminator. In the meantime the premises will be closed down.

FLIES

Flies are dangerous! Do you know what happens when a fly lands on your food? First it vomits digestive juices, then it 'dances' to work the juices into the food so that it can suck the mixture and feed. As the fly 'dances', bacteria picked up from dead animals or faeces drop from its legs. Now it's your customer's turn to eat.

Many diseases are carried by flies and they are a constant cause of cross-contamination and so are a serious hazard to food safety. Flies must be prevented from entering the kitchen by the use of a fly curtain and the room should be fitted with an electric fly zapper to kill any that do manage to get in.

An example of an electric fly zapper

Always remember that you must *not* use pesticides in or near the kitchen due to the danger of their contaminating food.

HOUSEHOLD PETS

Pets such as dogs and cats carry bacteria on their coats and paws, and must be kept away from food storage and preparation areas. Domestic cats and dogs can carry the deadly strain of E. coli, and a cat or dog can also cause cross-contamination which may lead to a serious food poisoning outbreak.

PEST PREVENTION

Do not let any pest sighting go unattended. Report it to your supervisor so that they can arrange for an exterminator and discard all food that may have been in contact with pests. Inspect delivery vans for signs of pests, as well as any food packaging. Keep all rubbish areas very clean; outside rubbish will attract pests, which will then enter the kitchen.

Never give pests a chance – keep the kitchen clean and outside areas free of rubbish at all times.

Pests are attracted to food debris, so remember to clean as you go

CLEANING

Cleaning safely means
cleaning in places you
cannot see

A clean kitchen is one that has been thoroughly cleaned to prevent the contamination of food by living and non-living contaminants, both bacterial and material (eg chemicals and particles from metal and glass).

High-priority cleaning should be given to items that are frequently touched, such as taps and door handles. These should be cleaned more than once a day to prevent contamination and should be allowed to dry naturally after every shift. Allowing items to dry naturally removes the chance of contamination by using towels.

A kitchen must be properly cleaned and sanitised, following the instructions provided with the cleaning agents.

The following six-point cleaning plan can be adapted by using different companies' cleaning products. Stages 2, 3 and 4 may be combined in a single specialised cleaning product, and Stages 5 and 6 may be combined with the use of a surface sanitiser.

1   *Pre-clean:* remove all debris and loose dirt (eg sweep floors, wipe work surfaces).
2   *Main clean:* remove grease and waste using detergent and appropriate cleaning materials with hot water.
3   *Rinse:* remove detergent and leave clean.
4   *Disinfect:* with appropriate chemical spray.
5   *Final rinse:* with potable water to remove all traces of disinfectant.
6   *Dry:* air dry or use disposable towels to avoid the chance of contamination by reusable towels.

Clean and disinfect your work area after each task

Sanitisers combine detergents with a bactericide – a solution that kills bacteria, so they do two jobs at once. Always follow the manufacturer's instructions. Heat, such as hot water, aids cleaning and kills bacteria, and the use of heat is known as *thermal energy*. To remove more stubborn dirt, rubbing is needed, and this is known as *kinetic energy*.

A cleaning schedule will help staff to be aware of how frequently different items must be cleaned and whose responsibility it is to perform these tasks and check they have been done. A useful method is to name an area to be cleaned (eg a fridge or freezer) after a day of the week, which will be the day that item is always thoroughly cleaned.

Never store chemicals in the same area as food. Keep all cleaning solutions in a separate cupboard – they will harm your customers if eaten

Week Commencing.............................

Daily Cleaning Schedule														
	Monday		Tuesday		Wednesday		Thursday		Friday		Saturday		Sunday	
	√/x	Sig	√/x	Sig	√/x	Sig	√/x	Sig	√/x	Sig	√/x	Sig	√/x	Sig
All work surfaces														
Sinks														
Dishwasher														
Microwaves														
Overhead grill														
Bain-marie														
Hot lamps														
Internal bins														
Walls wiped														
Fridges wiped down														
Canopy wiped down														
Underneath work benches														
Oven tops wiped														
Drains swilled														

A cleaning schedule helps to ensure a clean kitchen

Wherever possible use disposable cloths, *especially* for drying. Good cleaning must never aid cross-contamination and using soiled towels will transmit dangerous bacteria.

To keep the kitchen clean, always adhere to the following steps.

1. Always clean as you work.
2. Make sure that your work area is cleaned and disinfected after each task and that all waste is cleared away.
3. Ensure your work space is as clean and uncluttered as possible as otherwise this could lead to cross-contamination and is a hazard.
4. Try to leave tasks such the preparation of raw meat until last. Always thoroughly clean and disinfect the work area immediately after preparing or handling raw meat.

Detergents will only destroy a bacterium's *environment*, by dissolving grease and removing bacterial film. They do *not* kill bacteria – that is the function of a sanitiser.

Some more points to bear in mind:

1   At the end of each shift the *entire* kitchen must be cleaned. This includes all work surfaces, the walls (where food debris and grease may have collected), the floors and all the equipment. Always use a good cleaning plan so that everyone is aware of their duties.

2   Always adhere to the six-point cleaning plan above.

3   Always ensure that cleaning agents, detergents and disinfectants cannot contaminate food. Store food away before use and always follow the manufacturer's instructions.

4   All manufacturer information on usage, storage, safety precautions and the potential hazards of cleaning agents must be clearly displayed on *material safety data sheets*, which are supplied with such products.

5   Cleaning checks should be made by a competent person so that cleaning standards are maintained and records kept, to ensure *due diligence*.

6   Records of cleaning and inspection should be constantly maintained. The results of monitoring with swabs and other mechanisms to measure bacterial levels must also be documented.

Always wear recommended safety equipment

CONTROL OF SUBSTANCES HAZARDOUS TO HEALTH

The control of substances hazardous to health (COSHH) is a law which protects employees and customers from harmful chemicals. These include the chemicals used to clean kitchens. Some of these are poisonous and some are harmful to the skin and eyes, especially if used in the wrong concentrations, so correct safety procedures must always be followed and the chemicals kept in locked storage, away from food.

PREMISES AND EQUIPMENT

The design of kitchens and food storage areas starts with thinking about avoiding contamination – how different foods can be processed without coming into contact with each other. 'Straight-line planning' (ie where the food is processed in sequence) leads to a workflow which keeps food such as raw meat and ready-to-eat foods separate. Similarly, a simple and direct route for the removal of waste from the kitchen is essential.

Everything should be designed for easy cleaning. Stainless steel is the usual material for work surfaces because it is impervious to liquids, and easy to clean and sanitise. The use of different-coloured chopping boards helps to avoid cross-contamination, and any broken or damaged equipment should be replaced.

Stainless steel kitchen work surfaces are used for easy cleaning

- The kitchen should have clean, smooth services without crevices or cracks (where pests can gather and breed), and any damage to plaster must be repaired.
- All windows should be easy to clean and – if opened – equipped with fly screens.
- Floor surfaces must be hard-wearing, non-absorbent and easy to clean. Specially designed flooring with a curved edge against the wall is much easier to keep clean than standard flooring.
- Waste storage areas should be easy to clean and designed for easy access by waste-removing vehicles, and waste should be stored in containers with secure lids to prevent infestation by pests and birds.
- Hand-washing facilities must be properly equipped with hot water, soap, a nail brush and disposable towels.

Remember to clean as you work

MEASURING TEMPERATURES

There are many excellent automatic systems for measuring temperatures in ovens and refrigerators. For food itself you can use a temperature probe, which must be carefully handled. The tip of the probe is pushed into the food item you are measuring and will become contaminated by bacteria. You should therefore have different probes designated for different tasks (i.e. food types), and each probe must be sterilised with a clean sanitised wipe before and after each use. You must allow the temperature to settle for about 30 seconds before taking a reading.

Probes should be calibrated and checked regularly to ensure they are working accurately. This is simply done: immerse the probe in boiling water and it should read 100°C; in slushy ice it should read 0°C.

Regularly check that your probes are working correctly

TRAINING AND THE LAW

The law requires that all people handling food are supervised in and trained for the work they perform, and that all employees who apply HACCP as required by law are trained in its application and principles.

LEGAL REQUIREMENTS

The following points are required by law:

- All food handlers must be trained and supervised.
- All chilled food must be held below 8°C but best practice is lower, *below 5°C.*
- All hot food being held for service must be above 63°C.
- Hand basins must be provided, with hot water, soap and disposable towels.
- All food handlers who are ill or have a skin cut must report this to their supervisor.
- All food handlers must be personally clean and wear protective clothing.
- Food premises must be suitably designed for the preparation of food.
- Food premises must have good hygiene and proper pest control.
- All premises must be in good repair.
- All equipment must in good working order and clean, to minimise the possibility of contamination.
- All equipment must be designed to enable thorough cleaning. Wherever possible equipment should be moveable so that staff can easily clean underneath and behind it.
- Waste must not accumulate and must be disposed of in proper closable containers.

These are the basic points of the law. A good rule of thumb is that if quality equipment is used in a well-designed building, cleaning and adherence to the law is easier. If it's easier to clean, a premises is more likely to be cleaned more often. Hence a well-designed and equipped kitchen is a safer kitchen.

You must know the legal requirements concerning food safety

If broken, the law imposes serious penalties, including fines on conviction of £20,000 and imprisonment for six months. Serious offences can attract unlimited fines and imprisonment for two years. The main offences under the Food Safety Act 1990 are:

- rendering food injurious to health (section 7 of the Act);
- selling, to the purchaser's prejudice, food which is not of the nature or substance or quality demanded (section 14); and
- falsely or misleadingly describing or presenting food (section 15).

HACCP is required to be practised by law. All food businesses must register with their local authority 28 days before opening and have a food safety management system in operation based on the principles of HACCP. All staff handling food must be trained for food safety and to comply with the law which states "Requirement that food business operators put in place, implement and maintain a permanent procedure or procedures based on the HACCP principles." (Article 5(1) of Regulation 852/2004).

In the next section you will learn how easy it is to apply HACCP as part of your everyday working routine. HACCP is there to help you, not hinder you. Think of it as a useful reminder system that ensures you work cleanly and safely and keep the required records. Simple!

HACCP: THE KEY TO FOOD SAFETY

THE SEVEN PRINCIPLES OF HACCP

The HACCP principles became law in 2006 and all food businesses *must* apply a food safety system based on them.

At first HACCP may seem a little complex, but it will soon fall into place as you read on. To begin, we can split the abbreviation into two parts:

- **HA:** hazard analysis – how we identify all possible risks.

- **CCP:** critical control point – the CCP for cooking food is 75°C and no cooked food should be served at a temperature below this. As mentioned above the exact temperature of cooked food can be measured using a probe.

The seven principles of HACCP are as follows:

1 **Identify all the hazards (physical, chemical, microbiological and allergenic).** List the preventive measures for each hazard. A food safety hazard is anything that affects the safety and quality of food and could endanger the health of a consumer. They can originate in the ingredients, the production process or the final product itself.

2 Identify the critical control points (CCPs). There will be various points in the process where hazards exist, but not all of them can or need to be controlled. Food may contain bacteria when delivered, but as long as the food is heated thoroughly and sufficiently to kill all bacteria later on in the process, controlling the microbiological hazard on delivery is not critical. However, carrying out the heating step correctly is vital.

3 Determine control actions for each CCP. Once the critical control points have been identified, *control actions* can be decided and written down. Precise and clear measures and targets should be defined and documented for every CCP. The actions to be taken will obviously depend on the situation.

4 Establish the monitoring methods for each CCP. The control actions are then monitored at given intervals to ensure daily control of critical processes. Monitoring in food service relies on various temperature measurements (see page 40). Daily audits should be carried out to ensure equipment is set up and functioning correctly, that hygiene processes are completed satisfactorily and that food safety policy has been followed (eg proper food storage and labelling). The frequency of monitoring depends on the level of risk. All monitoring results should be recorded (see the next principle).

5 Establish a registration and documentation system (good record-keeping). Keeping records of all monitoring results and procedures is helpful to ensure, and to *show*, that you have taken all reasonable precautions to minimise risks. Good documentation endorses the quality of your work.

6 Establish the corrective actions for each CCP. For all CCPs, pre-planned corrective measures should be defined for situations when the control criteria are not met. For example if food has not been cooked well enough it should be cooked again or thrown out. The procedures to regularly measure the CCPs, as well as the responsible person for each task, need to be defined.

7 Verification – checking that the HACCP system works. Any food safety system needs to be kept up to date. Audits, microbial testing, review of documents and evaluations of employee training will help to ensure this and that the HACCP system is working well and comprehensively. You should regularly review whether your procedures are still being followed, are working properly and are stringent enough to ensure safety.

PLANNING

Food safety starts with planning and being prepared. It is always best to think and plan ahead: it saves time, effort and importantly energy, as we must all be considerate of our carbon footprint.

Below are the tasks you need to perform before preparing food. These include ensuring that you are healthy and properly prepared for work, and to know what you are preparing and for whom. This is followed by a hazard analysis to find out what could happen, especially the risk of food contamination, and how to avoid the chances of food poisoning.

PERSONAL HYGIENE AND HEALTH

Everyone becomes ill from time to time and will carry bacteria that could infect another person. Often this cannot be avoided, but the risk can be minimised. If a person is ill they *must not* handle or prepare food, or even work in the same room where food is being prepared by others (the person may sneeze, cough or touch food inadvertently). In this way they will transmit bacteria or viruses to their colleagues, which may in turn be passed on to customers. If you are unwell you must tell your supervisor.

Sadly we all know too well that occasionally chefs cut themselves. Any cut must be fully covered by a commercial blue waterproof plaster (blue is used because it is a very rare food colour, and therefore highly noticeable). A cut is likely to be infected with poisons that can contaminate your customer's food. Infections can also occur at sites of body piercing, so all body piercings must be covered, or better still removed and the hole covered to prevent transmission of infection.

Your hair must be clean and neat. If long it must be tied up, preferably under a hat. Hair can carry bacteria and so must be prevented from falling anywhere in the kitchen. *Never* comb or touch your hair when you are in the kitchen.

All jewellery including watches should be removed as these can harbour bacteria and may fall into food. You should also avoid wearing strong perfume, as this may be offensive to customers and fellow employees.

Clean protective uniforms should always be worn. They protect the food from the contamination which is often found on normal clothes.

You must report all the following illnesses:

■ diarrhoea
■ stomach pains or feeling unwell
■ nausea.

You must *always wash your hands:*

■ after visiting the toilet
■ before starting work or entering the kitchen
■ between jobs, especially after handling raw meat
■ after handling waste
■ after touching your face or sneezing
■ after cleaning
■ when you enter the kitchen and between *every job.*

All hand-washing basins must have hot water, a nail brush, soap and preferably disposable towels. Dirty towels are a potential contamination vehicle.

To wash your hands, wet them thoroughly and then completely cover them with soap. Rub hard between your fingers, make sure your nails are clean and if necessary use the nail brush. Rub and rotate your hands to ensure the soap reaches all areas. Rinse thoroughly and dry with a disposable towel. Do not use reusable towels. If the soap or towels run out, tell your supervisor.

HAZARD ANALYSIS

First the hazards – there are four types:

1   **Microbiological:** these are bacteria and viruses – living organisms that cause disease and death.

2   **Chemical:** these include cleaning chemicals, poisons for pest bait, etc.

3   **Physical:** steel wool, glass, metal parts (including jewellery).

4   **Allergens:** many people have an allergy to some types of food. The most common are peanuts, nuts and shellfish, although other foods, including apples, peaches and rice, can cause a life-threatening reaction. People with an allergy can react very quickly; an extreme reaction is called anaphylactic shock, where the body actually switches off. A person experiencing an anaphylactic reaction must be given immediate medical attention and the emergency services should be called without delay.

YOUR CUSTOMERS

You need to know who you are serving. You may be working in a general restaurant with all types of customer, or perhaps a care home for the elderly, a hospital or a kindergarten for young children. The last groups of people (the elderly, the sick and the very young) have a reduced immune system, meaning that their defence against disease and infection is lower. Therefore if you are preparing food in a hospital, care home or kindergarten, you should avoid serving any food type that is considered high risk.

Elderly people are more susceptible to food poisoning, so they should not be served high-risk foods

High-risk foods include:

- shellfish, especially raw
- unpasteurised dairy products such as unpasteurised cheese
- slightly cooked or rare foods, such as runny eggs
- foods that may contain allergens.

Some foods are considered high risk because they provide a good environment for bacteria to breed and can very easily become contaminated. For this reason the following foods are high risk for everyone:

- all cooked meats and poultry (they are an excellent growing environment for bacteria)
- high-risk foods include cooked rice, due to spores (see page 13) (meaning that bacteria can grow again *after* cooking)
- all egg-based foods and dairy products.

Now you are clear about your customer type and any foods that should be avoided as a result, the hazard analysis moves on to look at the risks of chemical contamination.

You must know which foods are high-risk for people with a reduced immune system

CHEMICAL CONTAMINATION

The two main sources of chemical contamination are:

- cleaning chemicals
- poisons for pest control.

Both should be kept away from food in a secure, locked storage unit, and they should only be accessed and used when all food is stored away. Before food preparation begins, any clothes staff were wearing when using chemicals or poisons *must* be changed.

PHYSICAL CONTAMINATION

Contamination can come from a physical source. For example:

- jewellery falling into food
- glass, steel wire from cleaning pads, and other metal utensils in the kitchen.
- plasters and hair (see page 28).

Some foods can contain contaminants such as stones, soil and insects, so it is always important to monitor the quality of all deliveries and to set supplier standards and specifications.

ALLERGENS

Many people are allergic to certain foods, so you must always be aware of all the ingredients contained in the food served by your kitchen. For example, many pre-prepared foodstuffs such as ice cream contain eggs, and other foods contain traces of nuts. Be very careful when garnishing food, because even if a pre-prepared food type is allergen free, if it is garnished with chopped nuts it can become fatal to certain people.

All members of staff should be trained in allergen awareness and observe the house rules, and everyone should be able to recognise the symptoms of an allergic reaction. Of course some restaurants serve shellfish and dishes containing nuts, and the key here is *awareness*: the staff must be aware of food ingredients and the customers likewise. It is very important that your supplier provides complete ingredient information and alerts you when any changes are made. It is also very important to *listen carefully to your customers*. If an allergy sufferer asks for information about the ingredients of a certain food it is essential that you understand them completely so that you can give an accurate response. *Never* guess!

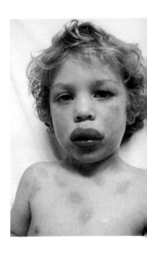

Allergies can cause an *anaphylactic shock*, which is life-threatening. The symptoms include:

- reddening of the skin, swelling of the lips and eyelids
- swelling of the throat, difficulty breathing and/or speaking
- feeling faint due to a serious drop in blood pressure
- nausea
- collapse and unconsciousness.

As noted earlier, if someone suffers these symptoms you must render immediate medical attention and call an ambulance.

At this stage we have processed our hazard analysis for the menu for our customers and have decided on the raw or prepared foods that we are purchasing. You will now understand how important it is to know exactly what foods you are buying and that they are supplied by reputable companies that can provide the fullest information. Your customers can become ill because of the food supplied, and it is the *restaurant's responsibility* to ensure that only good-quality, safe foods are served. A comprehensive hazard analysis and good staff awareness are vital in ensuring that this is the case.

You now have conducted your hazard analysis to the point of starting production. To appreciate the hazards at this stage we need to fully understand how bacteria can be controlled by limiting their environment, or in other words preventing their growth, and how to use the most important weapons: time and temperature.

RECEIVING AND STORING FOOD

RECEIVING FOOD

Clean designated receiving tables must be provided for all food. It is essential to keep raw meats away from ready-to eat-food such as salads, otherwise dangerous contamination can occur. It is very easy in a busy environment for delivered foods to come into contact with each other so great care must be taken at all times. Always use separate probes for different types of food: for example, never use a probe that has just measured raw meat such as chicken to measure the temperature of a ready-to-eat food. Do not bring packaging material into the kitchen because this may have become contaminated outside.

Record and check all food coming into the kitchen. All personnel responsible for receiving and storing must be fully trained and empowered to reject any food if it's too warm, damaged or showing signs of pests.

Every delivery must be checked – if you are using a clipboard to make an inventory of a delivery, make sure the clipboard itself is clean! This is good practice for quality and quantity as well as safety.

REJECTING FOOD

Food should be rejected if:

- the package is damaged
- there are signs of pests
- the temperature of fresh food is above 8°C. Some house rules specify a limit of 5°C
- the temperature of frozen food is warmer than −15°C.

Keep a record of all food received and returned, and periodically inspect delivery vans for signs of dirt and pest infestation.

First In **FIFO** First Out
Stock Rotation

STORING FOOD

It is important to store food as quickly as it can be put away. Remove outside packaging and store frozen foods first. Transport and store raw meat separately from ready-to-eat foods.

After you have received a food delivery it must be stored away quickly

Never tightly pack food in storage areas. It should be kept at least 15cm above the floor and at least 5cm away from the walls. This will make cleaning and pest inspections easier.

Keep a record of all food temperatures, and if you observe high temperatures report this immediately to your supervisor. This can be the result of a delay in storing food, allowing it to warm up to room temperature. Such delays can be avoided by having allocated time slots for staff to store food correctly.

Contamination is dangerous! You must remember to:

- keep raw meats in separate refrigerators or on the bottom shelf to avoid contaminating anything below
- clean soil from vegetables before storing them. Soil can contain dangerous bacteria
- check all seals of fridge and freezer doors are working properly and are clean. Fridges and freezers should be checked *every day* and detailed, stringent temperature records maintained.

Stock rotation is important. You should always practise *FIFO: first in, first out.* Label each item so that you know when it was delivered and its shelf life. Do not sell food that has passed its use-by date and make sure that all the correct storage requirements are followed (eg storing below a certain temperature).

Always check that fridge door seals are working

Always remember to:

- store all frozen foods within 15 minutes at below –18°C
- store all fresh food within 15 minutes at below 5°C
- store dry goods quickly

- keep fridge or freezer doors open for the shortest time possible
- immediately report any fridge or freezer malfunction – a breakdown is an expensive and serious hazard.

REFRIGERATOR TEMPERATURE LOG

Month _____ *20* _____
Refrigerator name _____ *Location* _____

Day	Time	Recorded by	External	Internal	Corrective action
1					
2					
3					
4					
5					
6					
7					
8					
9					
10					
11					
12					
13					
14					
15					
16					
17					
18					
19					
20					
21					
22					
23					
24					
25					
26					
27					
28					
29					
30					
31					

Optimal ranges: 3°C to 8°C

Please report readings that do not fall in the optimal ranges to a manager or supervisor.
Corrective action must be noted if temperatures fall outside of appropriate range.

A refrigerator temperature log, an example of a document needed for good record-keeping

Planning is important at all stages

Remember the dangerous temperature zone: 5°C to 63°C

Colour coded chopping boards

Colour coded chopping boards
Red - Raw meat
Blue - Raw fish
Yellow - Cooked meat
Green - Salad and fruit
Brown - Vegetables
White - Bakery and dairy

FOOD PREPARATION

When preparing raw foods, think *contamination*. Remember your hazard analysis and think about what can go wrong – even *dangerously* wrong. For example, if you prepare raw meat first and then a salad it is possible that traces of the meat will contaminate the salad. Therefore, you should prepare the salad *first*, cover it and refrigerate it before preparing the raw meat. Remember to use different coloured chopping boards. If this is not possible then anything that has been used to prepare the raw meat must be thoroughly cleaned and sanitised before ready-to-eat foods can be prepared in the same area.

Whatever food you are preparing, use the correct amount for the immediate task in order to prevent food being out of the fridge any longer than necessary.

Cooking temperatures kill bacteria, which is why all prepared foods must have a centre core temperature, as measured by a probe inserted into the innermost part of the food, of 75°C or above (in Scotland this temperature is 82°C).

When preparing food:

- never use the same utensils and working area for raw meats and salads or other ready-to eat-foods
- pass all chopping boards through the dishwasher after completing each task
- if food has not achieved the correct core temperature return it for further cooking and check the temperature again, repeating as necessary until the temperature is at or above 75°C
- always stir all liquids before checking their temperature
- always check food periodically during microwave cooking to ensure even cooking.

FOOD TEMPERATURE

A kitchen usually consumes more energy than any other room in the building, and this energy is vital for food safety. Refrigeration and freezing keep temperatures low and prevent bacterial growth. Blast chillers quickly lower temperatures to achieve the same result. Heat energy cooks food and kills bacteria. Therefore, it is always important to monitor and regulate temperature settings of cooking equipment, firstly to ensure food safety, and secondly to reduce their carbon footprint. Never switch on cooking equipment until it is needed. Modern equipment is designed to consume less energy and to only be turned on when in use.

THAWING FOOD

The first step in preparing food is to thaw it if it is frozen. If thawing is not performed thoroughly, this may result in undercooked parts of the meat, such as chicken, leaving harmful bacteria alive. Think ahead and remove what you know you will need from the freezer in good time to allow it to defrost in a refrigerator. It is therefore very important to know exactly how long a given food item will take to defrost properly.

If you need to defrost food quickly you can speed the process up by using cold running water. *Never* defrost under warm or hot water because this can allow bacteria to grow and produce dangerous toxins (a good example is scombrotoxin which is preserved in frozen fish).

Always remember to:

- test each piece of cooking equipment to calculate how long it takes to reach cooking temperature. This means that you will only switch the equipment on when it is needed. Although by necessity kitchens use a lot of energy this does not mean that they have to be unnecessarily wasteful

- check, every shift, the operating temperatures of all refrigerators and freezers. Make a note of any temperature increases and consider whether you can alter your work routine to maintain a lower temperature (eg by knowing exactly what you need to retrieve from the fridge or freezer *before* you open the door)

- put a drip tray underneath thawing meat and only ever defrost meat on the bottom shelf

- check the temperature of food before cooking.

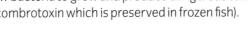

Planning keeps you cool, the kitchen cool, and saves time

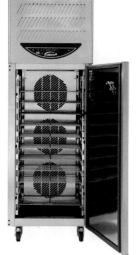

HOLDING AND SERVICE

The best way to serve hot food is to serve it immediately, but if you must hold it *before* service, then there are three ways in which you can do so:

- *Hot holding:* all hot food must be held above 63°C to prevent bacteria from starting to grow. All temperatures must be recorded several times each service as part of HACCP due diligence.

- *Cook chill:* this means chilling food that will be served later. All hot food must be chilled as quickly as possible to prevent bacterial growth in the dangerous temperature zone. Reducing the portion size aids cooling. Food should be chilled using a blast chiller to ensure that it is cooled to below 10°C within 90 minutes and to 5°C within four hours.

- *Cold holding:* all cold foods must be kept below 8°C but best practice recommends below 5°C, especially for meats and seafood. The maximum holding time using this method is four hours.

Action points to remember are:

- immediately serve hot food

- chill all food quickly within 90 minutes to 10°C, and label and place in the refrigerator

- keep all foods out of the dangerous temperature zone

- record all temperatures several times each service to comply with the HACCP record system and due diligence.

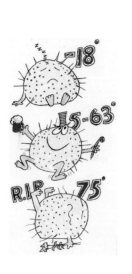

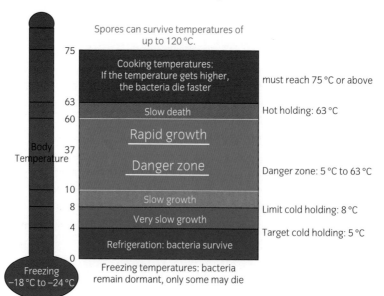

Spores can survive temperatures of up to 120 °C.

75
Cooking temperatures:
If the temperature gets higher, the bacteria die faster — must reach 75 °C or above

63
60 — Slow death — Hot holding: 63 °C

Rapid growth

Body Temperature 37
Danger zone — Danger zone: 5 °C to 63 °C

10
8 — Slow growth — Limit cold holding: 8 °C

Very slow growth

4 — Target cold holding: 5 °C

Refrigeration: bacteria survive

0

Freezing
−18 °C to −24 °C

Freezing temperatures: bacteria remain dormant, only some may die

Life cycle thermometer for bacteria

CHECKING AND VERIFICATION

To recap, the seven points are:

1 Identify the hazards.

2 Identify the critical control points (CCPs).

3 Determine control actions for each CCP.

4 Establish the monitoring method for each CCP.

5 Establish a registration and documentation system (good record-keeping).

6 Establish the corrective actions for each CCP.

7 Verification – checking that the HACCP system works.

In practical terms this means:

1 Performing a hazard analysis and being aware of what you are cooking and for whom.

2 Establishing the critical point to measure, such as the warmest temperature for a refrigerator, or the core temperature for processed foods.

3 Knowing the limits of what is an acceptable reading. If the reading is unacceptable, Point 6, corrective action, comes into play.

4 Establishing monitoring methods always relates to measuring the temperature, but you may choose to include other factors such as the length of time it has taken to chill food.

5 Keeping records so that you know what has to be measured and when. This is important to ensure that corrective action has been taken and that you have worked according to good practice for your customers' well-being.

6 Being aware of what to do if something is wrong (eg, too low a cooking temperature, reheat; food past its use-by date, discard; a delivery that is too warm, return). All staff should be empowered to take corrective action and to record that action.

7 Checking to ensure your system works to the highest standards. It's no use having a system that is never checked. HACCP is a complex system that takes time and so it needs to be checked that it is working. A system may need to change if different foods are purchased, or menus alter. Everyone needs to be involved. HACCP is not just for management, it is for everyone. It can only function properly when the team is working together.

HACCP will help you in your work by reminding you of how and when to perform important tasks, which you will record and can later consider. It is the key to ensuring that food is always prepared as safely as possible.

Working together results in a safe and happy kitchen

MORE HELP AND INFORMATION

Now you have learned how and why it is important to follow good practice and HACCP in your daily work. You may still feel uncertain at times which is why it will be helpful to keep this book with you at work.

If you'd like to learn more, a highly recommended food safety publication is the *Safer Food Better Business* guide published by the Food Standards Agency. You can download a PDF by visiting the Food Standards Agency's website at www.food.gov.uk and search for SFBB. This document will help turn what you have learned in this book into everyday good working practice.

The Food Standards Agency site contains lots of other useful information – just type into the search box what you want to know.

The Catering Equipment Suppliers Association (CESA) is an excellent source for information on equipment. Their website is: www.cesa.org.uk.

If you are interested in kitchen design, visit the Foodservice Consultants Society International (FCSI) website at www.fcsi.org and select your location.

TEST YOUR KNOWLEDGE

Use the questions below to test your knowledge of the Level 2 Award in Food Safety to see how much information you have retained. These questions will help you to revise what you have learned in this book.

Notes

1. Why is it important to follow food safety systems and procedures?

○ a   To prevent illness
○ b   To reduce pest infestation
○ c   To maintain a good working environment
○ d   Because it is the law

2. What should you use for rinsing?

○ a   Any tap water
○ b   Potable water
○ c   A cleaning solution
○ d   A sanitiser

3. Why is it important to have your hair tied neatly or wear a hat?

○ a   Because hair can transport bacteria
○ b   Because hair can drop out
○ c   To look tidy
○ d   Because it is unsafe

4. Below what temperature should a refrigerator operate?

○ a   8°C
○ b   5°C
○ c   3°C
○ d   12°C

5. Why should you not touch your mouth or eat in the kitchen?

- a   Because you must not eat the customers' food
- b   Because you will get indigestion
- c   Because you could contaminate your customers' food
- d   Because it is messy and will attract pests

6. Which of the following is the most likely way for a food handler to carry bacteria from one food to another?

- a   By wearing their uniform outside
- b   By not washing hands frequently
- c   By not wearing the correct protective clothing when handling food
- d   By wearing outside shoes in the kitchen

7. Why should kitchen uniforms not be worn outside?

- a   Because people will know that you are a food handler
- b   Because the uniform may get contaminated with bacteria
- c   Because the uniform may become dirty
- d   Because it is the house rules

8. Why is hand washing so important?

- a   Because we must only work with clean hands
- b   Clean hands are good kitchen practice
- c   Hands carry bacteria that can easily be passed onto our customers' food.
- d   Because it is the house rules

9. Why should jewellery not be worn in the kitchen?

- a   Because it can fall off
- b   Because it can harbour bacteria
- c   Because it does not look professional
- d   Because it is not so easy to wash your hands

10. What colour chopping board must be used for raw meat?

- ○ a   Brown
- ○ b   Yellow
- ○ c   Red
- ○ d   White

11. Why are chopping boards a significant hazard?

- ○ a   Because they can facilitate cross-contamination
- ○ b   Because they are used for different tasks
- ○ c   Because they are continuously used and not always properly washed
- ○ d   Because they are always out in the warmth of the kitchen

12. A slicing machine must be sanitised

- ○ a   After each use or at the end of each preparation period
- ○ b   Every two hours
- ○ c   Each shift change
- ○ d   Only after slicing potentially hazardous foods

13. People such as your colleagues can carry a disease without showing any symptoms or illness, true or false?

- ○ a   True
- ○ b   False

14. A kitchen sanitiser is a mixture of

- ○ a   Detergent and soap
- ○ b   Detergent and disinfectant
- ○ c   Disinfectant and soap
- ○ d   Detergent and water

15. Which two of the following hazards are likely to be the result of improper cleaning?

1) Steel wire in the food
2) Chemical contamination
3) Glass in the food
4) Salmonella

○ a 1 & 4
○ b 2 & 3
○ c 1 & 2
○ d 3 & 4

16. Which of the following are most likely when a kitchen is suffering from a pest infestation?

1) Debris behind the kitchen equipment
2) Unpleasant smells
3) Faeces
4) Egg cases

○ a 1 & 4
○ b 1, 3 & 4
○ c 2, 3 & 4
○ d 1 & 2

17. When cooking processed foods or reheating foods, what should the core temperature reach before serving?

○ a 85°C
○ b 75°C
○ c 72°C
○ d 63°C

18. Why is time important?

○ a Because bacteria breed rapidly
○ b Because the higher the cooking temperature and the longer the cooking time the more bacteria are killed
○ c Because bacteria at room temperature grow to high numbers in a short time
○ d All of the above

19. At what temperature should frozen foods be stored?

- ○ a 0°C or colder
- ○ b −7°C or colder
- ○ c −12°C or colder
- ○ d −18°C or colder

20. Why is it important to use drip trays when thawing food?

- ○ a Because it's tidier and keeps the fridge clean
- ○ b Because it prevents fluids coming into contact with utensils and food
- ○ c Because it prevents leakage onto the floor
- ○ d Because it's easier to carry food

21. What is the maximum temperature for receiving frozen foods?

- ○ a Below −15°C
- ○ b Below −8°C
- ○ c Below −18°C
- ○ d Below 0°C

22. Why is it necessary to avoid the contamination of ready-to-eat foods?

- ○ a Because they can poison customers
- ○ b Because they have a limited shelf life
- ○ c Because they will not go through a critical control point to kill bacteria
- ○ d Because they are usually served cold or chilled

23. Which of the following must be reported to your supervisor?

1) Headache
2) Stomach pains
3) Diarrhoea
4) Infected cut
5) Backache
6) Cramp

○ a 1, 5 & 6
○ b 2, 3 & 4
○ c 3, 5 & 6
○ d 1, 4 & 6

24. What best describes 'due diligence'?

○ a Ensuring that paperwork is neat and available
○ b Keeping records to show that all temperatures were correct
○ c Keeping records on all aspects of food safety procedures on a daily basis
○ d Keeping records on all employees and suppliers

25. What is the best way to dispose of spoilt food?

○ a Quickly remove the spoilt portion and use the rest
○ b Discard in the bin and sanitise the storage area
○ c Discard in the bin
○ d Use spoilt food to save money and reduce waste

26. Why must food that has been displayed for four hours be discarded?

○ a Because it has lost its food value
○ b Because it has lost its flavour
○ c Because bacterial growth may have occurred
○ d Because bacterial spores may have formed

27. **What is the dangerous temperature zone for bacterial growth?**

○ a 63°C to 75°C
○ b 8°C to 63°C
○ c 8°C to 75°C
○ d 5°C to 63°C

28. **Which of the following is most likely to reduce the risk of bacterial food poisoning?**

○ a High pH
○ b Removal of air
○ c Correct time/temperature management
○ d Following your manager's advice

29. **Which group of hazards mentioned below are the most frequent causes of food-borne illnesses?**

○ a Chemical hazards (eg pesticide residue)
○ b Physical hazards (eg foreign material)
○ c Microbiological hazards (eg dangerous bacteria)
○ d Mistakes made by people

30. **Food waste should be removed**

○ a Only when all cooking is completed
○ b Constantly, to inside bins
○ c By the cleaning staff
○ d Constantly, to outside bins

GLOSSARY

acid a clear liquid that has a pH lower than 5. An example of an acidic liquid is lemon juice.

aerobe any organism that requires oxygen to produce energy.

aflatoxin a toxin produced by the mould *Aspergillus flavus*. It is found in peanuts, soybeans, wheat, barley, sorghum and various nuts. Ingestion can cause weight loss, convulsions and liver damage.

allergen a protein which will cause an inappropriate immune response, making a person ill if they have an allergy to food containing that protein. People can also be allergic to non-food items such as dust mites and latex.

allergy allergies are caused by an inappropriate immune response to a substance such as a food item (eg peanuts, shellfish). Typical food allergens should be treated as a kitchen hazard and accurate information on all foods should be provided to the customer on request.

anaerobe a bacterium that does not require oxygen to produce energy. Some species are able to switch their systems between aerobic and anaerobic respiration to survive in difficult conditions.

atmosphere the air around us, which contains many gases, including oxygen and carbon dioxide. Also found in the atmosphere are microorganisms including bacteria and mould spores. Therefore you only have to leave uncovered food open to the air to risk contaminating it.

bacteria a group of single-celled microorganisms responsible for most cases of food poisoning. Bacteria have the ability to evolve rapidly and survive in difficult conditions which is why we practise food safety.

carrier a person who does not show symptoms of an illness but can pass the infection to others. Such a person must never work near food.

cockroach a beetle-like insect whose activities are nocturnal, meaning they can often be overlooked during the day. These are a major disease-carrier.

colony a group or collection of living organisms.

convection current the process by which heat moves through a fluid or liquid. Liquids are not heated uniformly so require stirring, thus creating convection currents, otherwise cool spots will occur that may allow bacteria to survive.

critical control point a stage in food preparation where a hazard is either eliminated or reduced to a safe level. An example is when food is cooked to a high enough temperature to kill harmful bacteria.

cross-contamination the process by which one food, or utensil, or working surface, or uniform, or hands can contaminate (infect) another food. This is a serious hazard when infection is passed between raw and cooked food. The harmful bacteria on raw meats will be transmitted to cooked food, leading to deadly food poisoning.

dormant the stage when an organism is not developing or growing but waiting until the environment becomes suitable for growth and multiplication.

due diligence kitchens need to demonstrate due diligence by means of meticulous record-keeping. Records are vital for food safety and may be used as evidence in the event of criminal proceedings. Due diligence is demonstrated by comprehensive records, good training and education of staff, the use of date stamps and date checks, routine hygiene inspections and audits and regular cleaning routines.

FIFO 'first in, first out': a simple way of remembering how to apply good stock rotation.

food hazard anything that may cause harm to a person who eats the food. The four types of hazard are:
1 microbiological – bacteria and viruses
2 physical – steel wool, jewellery, etc
3 chemical – cleaning fluids, pest baits and poisons
4 allergens – peanuts, nuts, shellfish, etc.

gastroenteritis a term to describe food poisoning with diarrhoea.

hazard analysis critical control point (HACCP) the legally required food safety system. There are seven principles:
1 Identify all hazards.
2 Identify the critical control points (CCPs).
3 Determine control actions for each CCP.
4 Establish the monitoring methods for each CCP.
5 Establish a registration and documentation system.
6 Establish the corrective actions for each CCP.
7 Verification – checking that the HACCP system works.

immune system the system in our bodies that combats disease. Our immune systems do not work so well when we are older or ill, or when we are very young. This is why it is vital to know who we are serving so that we can safely plan menus and identify hazards.

nutrients substances within food that organisms need to survive and grow.

outbreak where a number of people suffer from the same illness, such as food poisoning.

oxygen an odourless, colourless gas which sustains life. It is also necessary for the survival of many food-poisoning pathogens.

pathogen disease-causing microorganism.

pH a measure of the alkalinity or acidity of a solution. Items with a low pH are known as acids. Alkaline solutions are at the other end of the scale with a high pH value and include cleaning solutions that can dissolve fats.

ready-to-eat food all food that will not be cooked (or processed) to kill bacteria. It must never come into contact with bacteria such as those found on raw meat.

reconstitute to build up from parts. In food preparation this frequently refers to the addition of water, such as in the reconstitution of powdered milk.

sanitiser a combined chemical cleaning and bactericide used to kill most bacteria.

spore a spore develops from a bacterium in adverse conditions such as rising temperatures. The spore will survive and, when the food cools, will open, allowing bacteria to grow once again.

toxin a poison secreted/produced by microorganisms including bacteria.

virus a very small living parcel of protein that needs a host cell to copy itself (multiply). The Norwalk virus (norovirus) causes gastroenteritis, especially in confined environments such as cruise ships where the virus is easily passed from person to person. This is why personal hygiene, especially hand-washing, is so important.

The City & Guilds
Food Safety Training Manual
Level 2 Award in Food Safety in Catering

Training of staff

Date _____

Training record _____

          (name of member of staff to be inserted here)

          _____

          (name of employer/trainer name/tutor and address of premises
          where training was carried out to be inserted here)

The training record is to certify that the above named member of staff has completed the necessary course requirements to achieve the certificate for the Level 2 Award in Food Safety in Catering (QCF) (7150).

This form is to confirm that the above named member of staff can understand how individuals can take personal responsibility for food safety, understand the importance of keeping him/herself clean and hygienic, understand the importance of keeping the work areas clean and hygienic and understand the importance of keeping food safe as per the learning outcomes of the qualification and current European Union legislation relating to working in a food handling environment.

Declaration

Trainee   I, _____ (name of member of staff)
               confirm that I have received the minimum level of training as required by the FSA and the EU enabling me to undertake my responsibilities within the work environment.

Trainer   I, _____ (name of trainer)
               confirm that I have provided the above named member of staff with the minimum level of training as required by the FSA and the EU enabling them to undertake their responsibilities within the work environment.

Undertaking the learning within this training manual will enable the employee/learner to achieve the full qualification at Level 2, titled Level 2 Award in Food Safety in Catering. It will also give a good basis for further learning to achieve the Level 3 Award in Supervising Food Safety in Catering. To find out more go to www.cityandguilds.com and search for qualification code 7150.

Now that you have successfully completed the learning and activities to understand your role within this critical area, it is recommended that this learning is repeated and updated a minimum of every 3 years. Food safety is paramount to the welfare of every individual and you must be mindful of this every day. To order more copies of *The City & Guilds Food Safety Training Manual* go to www.cityandguildsbookshop.com or the Walled Garden.